# The BABY-SITTERS CLUB

## Kristy's Great Idea

# Ann M. Martin

# The BABY-SITTERS CLUB

# Kristy's Great Idea

### A GRAPHIC NOVEL BY
# RAINA TELGEMEIER

AN IMPRINT OF

**■SCHOLASTIC**

NEW YORK   TORONTO   LONDON   AUCKLAND   SYDNEY   MEXICO CITY   NEW DELHI   HONG KONG   BUENOS AIRES

Library of Congress Cataloging-in-Publication Data is available.

ISBN 0-439-80241-5 (hardcover)   ISBN 0-439-73933-0 (paperback)

10 9 8 7 6 5 4 3 2 1   06 07 08 09

First edition, April 2006
Lettering by Comicraft
Edited by David Levithan & Janna Morishima
Book design by Kristina Albertson
Creative Director: David Saylor
Printed in the U.S.A.

This book is for Beth McKeever Perkins,
my old baby-sitting buddy.
With Love
(and years of memories)
**A. M. M.**


Thanks to Dave, Mom, Dad, Amara, Will, Grandma, Diane, Bruce,
the Roman family, the Rigores family, the Cuevas family, K.C., Marisa,
Jason, my editors, my friends, my co-workers,
and my fellow comic artists.
**R. T.**

## Chapter 1

THE BABY-SITTERS CLUB. I'M PROUD TO SAY IT WAS TOTALLY MY IDEA, EVEN THOUGH THE FOUR OF US WORKED IT OUT TOGETHER.

"US" IS MARY ANNE SPIER, CLAUDIA KISHI, STACEY MCGILL, AND ME -- KRISTY THOMAS.

8

RRRRINNG!

HOORAY!!!

...MR. REDMONT?

I'M REALLY SORRY. I DIDN'T MEAN ANYTHING. I MEAN...

I DIDN'T **MEAN** I WAS GLAD SCHOOL WAS OVER, I MEANT I WAS GLAD I COULD GO HOME. BECAUSE MY HOUSE IS AIR-CONDITIONED...

BUT DO YOU THINK, KRISTY, THAT IT WOULD BE POSSIBLE IN THE FUTURE TO CONDUCT YOURSELF WITH A BIT MORE DECORUM?

..."DECORUM"?

YES, SIR.

GOOD.

BUT I WANT YOU TO REMEMBER THIS INCIDENT, AND THE BEST WAY FOR US TO REMEMBER THINGS IS TO WRITE THEM DOWN.

SO TONIGHT, I'D LIKE YOU TO WRITE A 100-WORD ESSAY ON THE IMPORTANCE OF DECORUM IN THE CLASSROOM.

DARN.

YES, SIR.

HEY.

MARY ANNE, HOW DO YOU EVER EXPECT TO BE ABLE TO WEAR NAIL POLISH IF YOU KEEP DOING THAT?

OH, COME ON. I'LL BE **75** BEFORE MY FATHER LETS ME WEAR **NAIL** POLISH.

MARY ANNE SPIER IS MY BEST FRIEND.

SHE'S VERY QUIET AND SHY, WHICH MY MOM SAYS IS BECAUSE MR. SPIER IS SO NERVOUS. MARY ANNE'S MOTHER DIED WHEN MARY ANNE WAS LITTLE.

MARY ANNE HAS NO BROTHERS OR SISTERS, SO SHE IS ALL HE'S GOT.

AT THEIR HOUSE, IT'S RULES, RULES, RULES. BUT YOU'D THINK THAT--

OH MY GOSH!!

WHAT IS IT?!

IT'S TUESDAY!!

14

15

GASP
GASP

DAVID MICHAEL?

WAAAH!!

WHAT'S WRONG?

I'M LOCKED OUT!

WHAT HAPPENED TO YOUR KEY?

I DON'T KNOW.

HEY, LOUIE!

WOOF! WOOF!

WHILE YOU GO TO THE BATHROOM, I'M GOING TO FIX US SOME LEMONADE, OKAY?

...OKAY!!

CLICK

RRRRRRRRRR

HEY...

HERE YOU GO!

HE-LLO-O!!

HEY, CHARLIE.

HI, EVERYBODY. HI, SQUIRT.

I AM **NOT** A SQUIRT.

ME AN' SAM ARE GOING TO PLAY SOME BALL AT THE HANSONS'. WANNA PLAY, KRISTY?

I DON'T KNOW -- I THOUGHT MARY ANNE AND I WOULD TAKE DAVID MICHAEL TO THE BROOK.

YOU WANT TO GO WADING, DAVID MICHAEL?

NOD

NOD

SEE YOU GUYS LATER!!

SLAM!

9:00, OKAY?

OKAY.

22

I'M HOME, KIDS!

I WONDER WHAT SHE WANTS....

YEAH...

HOW COME YOU BOUGHT A PIZZA, MOM?

!

KRISTYYY...

COME ON. WHAT DO YOU HAVE TO ASK US?

OH, ALL RIGHT. KATHY CALLED ME AT WORK TO SAY SHE WON'T BE ABLE TO WATCH DAVID MICHAEL TOMORROW. I WAS WONDERING WHAT YOU GUYS ARE--

FOOTBALL PRACTICE.

MATH CLUB.

SITTING AT THE NEWTONS'.

DRAT.

BUT WE **ARE** SORRY.

I KNOW YOU ARE.

HI, MARY ANNE? IT'S MRS. THOMAS.

I'M LOOKING FOR A SITTER TOMORROW AFTERNOON...

...SITTING AT THE PIKES'? OKAY.

HI, CLAUDIA?

...ART CLASS? I UNDERSTAND.

HELLO, CYNTHIA?

CHEERLEADING PRACTICE?

THAT'S WHEN IT HIT ME.

GOOD NEWS! MRS. NEWTON SAYS YOU CAN BRING DAVID MICHAEL WITH YOU TOMORROW WHEN YOU WATCH JAMIE, KRISTY.

...KRISTY?

UH, THAT'S GREAT, MOM.... CAN I PLEASE BE EXCUSED?

## Chapter 2

THIS LOOKS FINE, KRISTY.

DO YOU THINK IT'S OKAY THAT THE 99TH AND 100TH WORDS ARE "THE" AND "END"?

I HOPE SO.

OHH...9:00!

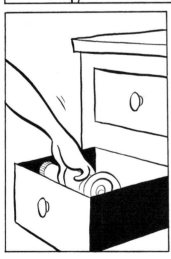

CLICK

FLASH

FLASH

FLAAAASH

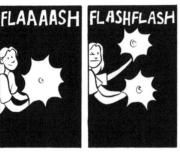
FLASHFLASH

FLA--

FLASH

"HAVE GREAT IDEA FOR BABY-SITTERS CLUB. MUST TALK. IMPORTANT. CAN'T WAIT. WE CAN GET LOTS OF JOBS."

"WHAT?"

FLASH...

"HAVE IDEA. BABY-SITTERS CLUB. MUST--"

"TERRIFIC. SEE YOU TOMORROW."

KNOCK KNOCK

COME IN?

CLICK

I JUST WANTED YOU TO KNOW...

I'M GOING OUT WITH WATSON ON SATURDAY NIGHT.

GROAN

I'M NOT ASKING FOR YOUR PERMISSION, KRISTY. I JUST WANT YOU TO BE ABLE TO PLAN ON MY BEING OUT SATURDAY.

CHARLIE'S GOT A DATE, BUT SAM WILL BE HOME.

MM.

I WISH YOU COULD BE A LITTLE MORE OPEN-MINDED ABOUT WATSON.

I CAN'T MAKE YOU LIKE HIM, BUT YOU HAVEN'T GIVEN HIM MUCH OF A CHANCE.

ONE MORE THING...

THIS IS WATSON'S WEEKEND TO HAVE HIS CHILDREN, AND HE HAS TO WORK SATURDAY MORNING....

HE WONDERED IF YOU'D BABY-SIT FOR ANDREW AND KAREN WHILE HE'S AT THE OFFICE.

NO WAY. WHY DO YOU KEEP ASKING?

I DON'T **WANT** TO WATCH WATSON'S KIDS.

I DON'T EVEN WANT TO **MEET** THEM. **EVER.**

OKAY... IT'S YOUR CHOICE.

GOING TO BED SOON?

YEAH. YOU CAN LEAVE THE DOOR OPEN.

GEEZ...WHAT IF MOM MARRIES WATSON?

SMILE 2004

WE'RE HAPPY THE WAY WE ARE.

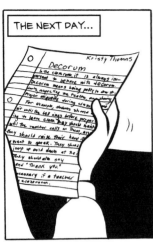

THE NEXT DAY...

THIS IS FINE, KRISTY. YOU EXPRESS YOURSELF NICELY ON PAPER.

LATER.

YOU'RE SITTING FOR THE PIKES TODAY?

YEAH!

HOW MANY OF THEM?

TWO. CLAIRE AND MARGO.

YOU SHOULD BRING THEM OVER TO THE NEWTONS'....THEY CAN PLAY WITH JAMIE AND DAVID MICHAEL.

## Chapter 3

OH, HEY, GREAT! AND YOU CAN TELL ME ABOUT THE BABY-SITTING CLUB.

OKAY! SEE YOU THERE.

SOON...

DING DONG!

HI-HI!

HI, JAMIE!

LOOK WHAT I GOT!

A G.I. JOE?!

GOT ANY OTHERS?

SURE! C'MON!

THANK GOODNESS FOR G.I. JOE.

37

HI-HI!

OKAY, SO TELL ME ABOUT THE BABY-SITTING CLUB!

WELL, I THOUGHT WE COULD GET TOGETHER WITH A COUPLE OTHER GIRLS WHO BABY-SIT...

...AND WE COULD FORM A CLUB.

SORT OF LIKE A COMPANY.

THUMP!

JAMIE!

WAAAH!

WHERE DOES IT HURT?

EVERYWHERE?

...YEAH.

MAYBE WE'D BETTER GO.

OKAY.

LISTEN, LET'S TELL CLAUDIA THE IDEA. I'LL MEET YOU AT HER HOUSE WHEN WE'RE DONE SITTING.

SHE'LL BE BACK FROM HER ART CLASS BY THEN.

OKAY... SEE YOU.

CLAUDIA!

YOUR FACE! YOU LOOK LIKE...

...YOU GOT MADE UP FOR THE CIRCUS. I MEAN, IT'S SO **COLORFUL!**

THANKS A **LOT.**

NO, HONESTLY, CLAUD... YOU DON'T **NEED** MAKEUP. YOU'VE GOT SUCH A BEAUTIFUL FACE.

NICE TRY.

UM... SO, WHERE'S YOUR SISTER?

THE GENIUS?

JANINE'S PROBABLY OUT STUDYING. WHERE ELSE?

MARY ANNE'LL BE HERE IN A FEW MINUTES. I HAVE THIS REALLY GREAT IDEA I WANT TO TELL BOTH OF YOU ABOUT.

WHAT IS IT??

A BABY-SITTERS CLUB.

A BABY-SITTERS CLUB?

YEAH, I'LL EXPLAIN IT ALL WHEN --

DING DONG!

AND IF, LIKE, MRS. PIKE WANTS **TWO** SITTERS, SHE ONLY HAS TO MAKE ONE CALL.

EXACTLY!

THERE'S ONLY TWO MORE THINGS TO THINK ABOUT:

ONE, WHERE SHOULD WE HOLD OUR MEETINGS?

AND TWO, WHO ELSE COULD WE ASK TO JOIN THE CLUB?

I CAN ANSWER **BOTH** QUESTIONS.

WE SHOULD HOLD MEETINGS HERE, BECAUSE I HAVE A PHONE IN MY ROOM.

OH, TERRIFIC!

AND I KNOW SOMEONE WHO MIGHT WANT TO JOIN THE CLUB.

WHO?

SHE'S NEW. SHE JUST MOVED TO STONEYBROOK. SHE LIVES RIGHT OVER ON FAWCETT AVENUE, AND SHE'S IN ONE OF MY CLASSES. HER NAME'S STACEY MCGILL.

WELL, OKAY . . . OF COURSE, WE'LL HAVE TO MEET HER.

OH, SURE. YOU'LL REALLY LIKE HER. SHE'S FROM NEW YORK CITY.

WHY DON'T WE ALL MEET HERE AGAIN AT 5:30 TOMORROW?

SOUNDS GOOD . . . SEE YOU THEN!!

THE NEXT DAY...

## Chapter 4

HEY, CLAUD!... NO MAKEUP TODAY, HUH?

MOM AND DAD WOULDN'T LET ME.

YOU GOT AWAY WITH THE SKULLS!

I PUT THEM ON WHEN I GOT TO SCHOOL. MIMI'S THE ONLY GROWN-UP HOME NOW, AND SHE DOESN'T MIND IF I WEAR SKULLS.

SNEAKY!!

STACEY'S ALREADY HERE. OH... AND JANINE'S HOME.

UGH!

AND HER DOOR'S OPEN --

OH, HI, KRISTY.

I THOUGHT I HEARD VOICES.

HI, JANINE.

47

CLAUDIA TOLD ME ABOUT THE BABY-SITTERS CLUB. THAT SOUNDS LIKE AN OUTSTANDING IDEA.

WELL, HOPEFULLY IT WILL --

KRISTY, "HOPEFULLY" IS ONE OF THE MOST COMMONLY MISUSED WORDS IN THE ENGLISH LANGUAGE. THE WORD MEANS "IN A HOPEFUL MANNER." IT IS NOT . . .

. . . ACCEPTABLE TO USE IT TO MEAN "IT IS TO BE HOPED." IF I WERE --

GEE, JANINE, I GOTTA GO. STACEY'S WAITING FOR US.

SEE YOU!

DING DONG!

THAT'S MARY ANNE! I'LL LET HER IN, CLAUD.

DON'T LOOK IN JANINE'S ROOM!

WHEW!

SLAM

49

JUST WHAT WE TALKED ABOUT YESTERDAY.

DID YOU BABY-SIT IN NEW YORK?

OH, ALL THE TIME.

WE LIVED IN THIS BIG BUILDING. THERE WERE OVER 200 APARTMENTS IN IT.

WOW!

I USED TO PUT UP SIGNS IN THE LAUNDRY ROOM. PEOPLE CALLED ME ALL THE TIME.

I CAN STAY OUT UNTIL 10:00 ON FRIDAY AND SATURDAY NIGHTS.

WOW!

I'D REALLY LIKE TO BE IN THE CLUB. I DON'T KNOW TOO MANY KIDS IN STONEYBROOK YET.

AND IT'D BE NICE TO EARN SOME MONEY... MY MOM AND DAD BUY MY CLOTHES, BUT THAT'S IT.

HOW COME YOU LEFT NEW YORK?

OH...

MY DAD CHANGED HIS JOB. **GOSH!** YOU HAVE A LOT OF NEAT POSTERS, CLAUDIA!

THANKS. I MADE THOSE TWO MYSELF. THEY'RE SILK-SCREENED.

BOY, IF I LIVED IN NEW YORK, I WOULDN'T LEAVE FOR **ANYTHING.**

TELL ME WHAT IT'S LIKE TO LIVE THERE. WHAT WAS YOUR SCHOOL LIKE?

WELL... I WENT TO A PRIVATE SCHOOL.

DID YOU HAVE TO WEAR A UNIFORM?

NOPE, WE COULD WEAR REGULAR CLOTHES.

HOW DID YOU GET TO SCHOOL?

ON THE SUBWAY.

WOW!!

WELL, ANYWAY, TO GET BACK TO THE BABY-SITTERS CLUB...

WHAT I THINK WE SHOULD DO IS MAKE TWO LISTS.

A LIST OF RULES, AND A LIST OF --

DOES THIS MEAN THAT I'M IN THE CLUB?

YUP.

OH, HEY, GREAT!!

SHUFFLE SHUFFLE

WE SHOULD CELEBRATE!

UM . . .

BUT IT'S NOT SAFE TO DIET IF YOU DON'T NEED TO.

MY MOM SAID SO. DOES YOUR MOTHER KNOW YOU'RE DIETING?

WELL, SHE --

SEE, I'LL BET SHE DOESN'T.

6:10!! OH, NO. DAD HATES IT WHEN I'M LATE... I HAVE TO GO.

WAIT!! WE DIDN'T FINISH MAKING OUR PLANS! LET'S MEET TOMORROW AFTER LUNCH, BY THE TETHERBALL COURT.

OKAY, SEE YOU GUYS THEN!

FRIDAY, LUNCHTIME

STACEY AND CLAUDIA SHOULD BE HERE SOON.

Thump

WHACK!

NOW THAT WE'RE ALL ACCOUNTED FOR...

...WE CAN DISCUSS THE NEXT PHASE OF OUR PLAN.

ADVERTISING. WE NEED TO LET PEOPLE KNOW WHAT WE'RE DOING. FLIERS WOULD BE THE EASIEST WAY.

WE CAN MAKE UP A NICE AD, AND MY MOM CAN COPY IT IN HER OFFICE.

THEN WE CAN PUT UP SIGNS AND FLIERS. ANYWHERE THAT'S IN BIKE-RIDING DISTANCE.

YOUR DAD WOULD LET YOU SIT IN ANOTHER NEIGHBORHOOD, RIGHT?

AS LONG AS IT'S NOT **TOO** FAR AWAY?

I GUESS SO.

GOOD. NOW . . .

WE ALREADY HAVE A NAME -- **THE BABY-SITTERS CLUB.** DO YOU THINK WE SHOULD HAVE SOME KIND OF SYMBOL OR SIGN, TOO?

YOU KNOW, LIKE THE SYMBOL THAT'S ON GIRL SCOUT COOKIES, OR THE SUN THAT'S ON THE STATIONERY MY MOM'S COMPANY USES?

YEAH! WE COULD PUT IT ON TOP OF OUR FLIERS.

CLAUDIA, YOU COULD DRAW SOMETHING FOR US.

I DON'T KNOW. . . .

COME ON, YOU'RE A GREAT ARTIST. YOU CAN DRAW ANYTHING.

I KNOW I CAN DRAW, BUT . . . BUT I'M NOT GOOD AT SYMBOLS AND STUFF. JANINE'S BETTER AT THOSE THINGS.

OH, FORGET JANINE.

ANYWAY, WE'RE ALL GOING TO THINK OF THE SYMBOL. WE'RE A CLUB. WE HAVE TO AGREE ON THINGS.

NOW WHAT SHOULD WE USE?

WELL . . .

IT COULD BE SOMETHING THAT HAS TO DO WITH BABY-SITTERS . . .

. . . LIKE A CHILD OR A HELPING HAND.

HOW ABOUT AN ALPHABET BLOCK WITH OUR INITIALS ON IT?

OH!

IT'S PERFECT, CLAUDIA! REALLY TERRIFIC!

YEAH!

RINNNNG!!

AW... WE GOTTA GO BACK TO CLASS.

THIS WEEKEND... WE WORK ON THE BABY-SITTERS CLUB!

## Chapter 5

SATURDAY.

HI, MRS. PIKE? THIS IS KRISTY THOMAS. I WANTED TO TELL YOU ABOUT A BUSINESS I'M STARTING!

MRS. NEWTON? IT'S MARY ANNE SPIER. KRISTY CAME UP WITH A GREAT NEW IDEA!

HI, MRS. SMITH? IT'S CLAUDIA KISHI FROM DOWN THE STREET. . . .

HELLO, STONEYBROOK NEWS? I'D LIKE TO PUT AN AD IN THIS WEEK'S PAPER.

WEDNESDAY? THAT SOUNDS GREAT!

OHH, I CAN'T WAIT!

HEY, YOU GUYS, I HAVE AN IDEA. I THINK WE SHOULD ELECT, YOU KNOW, OFFICERS OF THE CLUB.

OFFICERS?

YEAH. A PRESIDENT, A VICE PRESIDENT, A SECRETARY, AND . . . AND . . .

A TREASURER! PERFECT!

OH, I GET IT. WELL, I NOMINATE KRISTY FOR PRESIDENT. THE CLUB WAS HER IDEA.

I SECOND IT.

ME, TOO. IT'S UNANIMOUS.

WOW! THANKS, YOU GUYS. OKAY . . .

I NOMINATE CLAUDIA FOR VICE PRESIDENT SINCE WE'RE USING HER ROOM AND HER PHONE NUMBER.

SHE MAY GET A LOT OF CALLS TO HANDLE WHEN THE REST OF US AREN'T HERE.

I SECOND IT.

ME, TOO. UNANIMOUS AGAIN.

UM, STACEY, IF YOU DON'T MIND, I'D LIKE TO BE SECRETARY. I'M GOOD AT WRITING THINGS DOWN.

THAT'S PERFECT... I'M GOOD WITH MONEY AND NUMBERS. I WAS HOPING I COULD BE TREASURER.

GREAT!

YEAH!

OH, NO! I HAVE TO GO HOME, BUT I'LL BE RIGHT BACK.

STACEY, IF YOU'RE STILL ON THAT DUMB DIET, JUST SAY SO. YOU DON'T HAVE TO RUN AWAY.

NO, NO, IT'S NOT THAT....

LOOK, WE'LL PUT THE GUMMI BEARS BACK.

I JUST... I JUST FORGOT SOMETHING. IT'LL ONLY TAKE A MINUTE.

TWENTY MINUTES LATER...

WHERE IS IT?

WHERE'S WHAT?

WHAT YOU FORGOT.

OH! OH, NO, I JUST FORGOT TO **DO** SOMETHING. BUT IT'S ALL TAKEN CARE OF.

SO HOW CO --

STACEY, CHECK OUT THE FLIER WE MADE.

OOOH, LET'S SEE.

Need a baby-sitter? Save time!

CALL:  The
Baby-sitters
Club

# 555 - 0457

Monday, Wednesday, Friday 5:30 - 6:00
and reach four experienced baby-sitters.

Available: ★ Weekends
★ After School
★ Evenings

The Baby-sitters Club
555-0457
M-W-F 5:30-6:00

The Baby-sitters Club
555-0457
M-W-F 5:30-6:00

The Baby-sitters Club
555-0457
M-W-F 5:30-6:00

The Baby-sitters Club
555-0457
M-W-F 5:30-6:00

The Baby-sitters Club
555-0457
M-W-F 5:30-6:00

The Baby-sitters Club
555-0457
M-W-F 5:30-6:00

The Baby-sitters Club
555-0457
M-W-F 5:30-6:00

The Baby-sitters Club
555-0457
M-W-F 5:30-6:00

The Baby-sitters Club
555-0457
M-W-F 5:30-6:00

The Baby-sitters Club
555-0457
M-W-F 5:30-6:00

The Baby-sitters Club
555-0457
M-W-F 5:30-6:00

I GUESS I SHOULD GET GOING. IT'S ALMOST DINNERTIME, AND MY MOM'S GOING OUT WITH WATSON TONIGHT.

WHO'S WATSON?

MY MOM'S BOYFRIEND. MY PARENTS ARE DIVORCED.

OH.

ARE YOURS DIVORCED, TOO?

NOPE. THEY'VE BEEN MARRIED FOR 15 YEARS.

MINE HAVE BEEN MARRIED FOR 20 YEARS.

MY MOTHER DIED WHEN I WAS A BABY. SHE HAD CANCER.

IT'S ALL RIGHT, REALLY. I DON'T REMEMBER HER.

....

BUT SOMETIMES I WISH I DID.

I'D REALLY BETTER GO.

DING
DONG

KRISTY!
WATSON'S
HERE!

SLAM.

COMING.

CLUMP

CLOMP

SURPRISE!!

WHAT?

ISN'T THIS
NICE, KRISTY?
WATSON BROUGHT OVER
CHINESE FOOD!

WE CAN ALL EAT TOGETHER BEFORE HE AND I GO OUT.

WHO'S TAKING CARE OF **YOUR** KIDS?

I FOUND A VERY NICE BABY-SITTER.

SHE TOOK CARE OF ANDREW AND KAREN THIS MORNING WHEN I WENT TO THE OFFICE, AND THEY LIKED HER VERY MUCH.

OH.

SNIFFFF...

73

74

THE THING IS... WATSON IS ACTUALLY A VERY GOOD FATHER.

HE SEES KAREN AND ANDREW ALL THE TIME AND NEVER FORGETS HOLIDAYS...

...LIKE **MY** DAD DOES.

DEAR MOM, I'M SORRY I WAS SO RUDE. I GUESS I HAVEN'T LEARNED MUCH ABOUT DECORUM.

I HOPE YOU HAD FUN ON YOUR DATE. I LOVE YOU. -- KRISTY.

Need a sitter? Save time!
call: **B S C**
The Baby-Sitters Club
555-0457
Mon. Wed. Fri. 5:30-6

YAR
SA

THAT'S THE LAST FLIER!

NOW WE JUST SIT BACK AND WAIT FOR CALLS.

FRIDAY

The
BABY-
SITTERS
CLUB
Mon. Wed. - Fri.
5:30 - 6:00 PM

COME IN!

THE PHONE'S NOT GOING TO RUN AWAY, YOU KNOW.

I KNOW. I'M JUST SO EXCITED.

...SO AM I!!

BOUNCE

I'VE BEEN WAITING ALL WEEK FOR TODAY TO COME! OH, THIS HAS GOT TO WORK. WE'LL HAVE CUSTOMERS... WON'T WE??

KNOCK KNOCK

84

5:29...

RINNG

I DON'T BELIEVE IT!

I'LL ANSWER IT, I'LL ANSWER IT!!

RINNG RING

GOOD AFTERNOON. BABY-SITTERS CLUB.

KRISTY, IT'S YOUR MOTHER.

MOM!! THESE ARE OUR BUSINESS HOURS!

YOU'RE NOT SUPPOSED TO...

WHAT? YOU DO? OH. PLEASE HOLD FOR A MOMENT.

MOM NEEDS A SITTER FOR DAVID MICHAEL! KATHY CAN'T COME NEXT WEDNESDAY!!

I'VE GOT OUR APPOINTMENT BOOK RIGHT HERE. NOW LET'S SEE.

MARY ANNE, YOU HAVE A DENTIST'S APPOINTMENT THAT DAY, AND I HAVE ART CLASS.

KRISTY, THAT LEAVES YOU AND STACEY.

WHAT SHOULD WE DO?

JUST A SEC, MOM.

HE'S **YOUR** BROTHER.

BUT IF YOU TOOK IT, YOU'D GET TO KNOW SOME OTHER PEOPLE IN THE NEIGHBORHOOD. YOU'D PROBABLY MEET MY OLDER BROTHERS....

BROTHERS??

BUT WHAT'LL YOU DO WHILE I BABY-SIT? SIT AND WATCH?

HOPEFULLY, I'LL GET ANOTHER JOB.... HELLO, MOM?

STACEY WILL TAKE THE JOB! HEY, WHERE ARE YOU CALLING FROM? OH, THE OFFICE.

QUIT TYING UP THE LINE, KRISTY!

MOM, I HAVE TO GO.

RING!

CAN I ANSWER IT?!!

GOOD AFTERNOON, BABY-SITTERS CLUB.

...I THINK YOU HAVE THE WRONG NUMBER. THERE'S NO JIM BARTOLINI HERE.

RING!!!

YOU GET IT, KRISTY. YOU'RE THE PRESIDENT.

89

BABY-SITTERS CLUB... YES... YES... JUST A MOMENT, PLEASE.

DO ANY OF YOU KNOW A MRS. MCKEEVER ON QUENTIN COURT?

NO...

NOPE.

WHAT'S SHE GOT?

TWO KIDS, BUFFY AND PINKY.

BUFFY AND PINKY!

**BUFFY** AND **PINKY?!**

THEY'RE THREE YEARS OLD.... THEY MUST BE TWINS.

SHE NEEDS SOMEONE WEDNESDAY AFTERNOON.... I GUESS I'M THE ONLY ONE FREE.

I'LL DO IT. I'M GETTING CURIOUS ABOUT THEM.

FINE. SIGN YOURSELF UP FOR THE JOB.

RINNG!!

WOW, 5:55. ONE LAST CALL!

HELLO?... WHAT?!

IT'S SOME BOY ON THE PHONE. HE SAYS HIS NAME IS JIM BARTOLINI. HE WANTS TO KNOW IF THERE'VE BEEN ANY CALLS FOR HIM!

YOU'RE KIDDING!

WHAT?!

OH, **WAIT** A SECOND!!

SAM!! IS THAT YOU??

NO. IT'S JIM BARTOLINI. I WAS WONDERING IF --

SAM, YOU'RE A RAT!

THE NERVE!

IT'S NOT FUNNY!

SLAM

I WAS **NOT** HAPPY WHEN I GOT HOME.

RING!

HI, KRISTY! IT'S CLAUDIA. MRS. NEWTON CALLED TONIGHT. SHE NEEDED A SITTER FOR THURSDAY.

...YEAH?

SO I TOOK THE JOB!

THAT'S GREAT, CLAUD.

SO JUST 'CAUSE THE MAIN PHONE NUMBER IS HERS, SHE GETS FIRST CRACK AT EVERY JOB?

MRS. NEWTON **ALWAYS** CALLS ME FIRST. AT LEAST SHE **USED TO.**

WELL...AT LEAST I'VE GOT A NEW CLIENT! PINKY AND BUFFY MCKEEVER! I WISH IT WERE WEDNESDAY NOW!

## Chapter 7

WEDNESDAY AFTERNOON.

HI, STACE! C'MON IN! I'M LEAVING IN A MINUTE.

HERE'S-THE-KITCHEN-THE-DISHWASHER-IS-BROKEN-DAVID-MICHAEL-CAN-HAVE-A-SNACK-COOKIES-IN-THE-JAR-NOTHING-AFTER-4:30 . . .

. . . HE'S-ALLERGIC-TO-CHOCOLATE-OH-THERE'S-LOUIE-HE-WON'T-BE-ANY-TROUBLE-ALL-THE-PHONE-NUMBERS-ARE-ON-THE-BULLETIN-BOARD . . .

MOM'S-IS-ON-THE-PHONE-I'LL-BE-AT-THE-MCKEEVERS'-BABY-SITTING-THE-TV'S-IN-THE-PLAYROOM-DAVID-MICHAEL-LIKES-CANDYLAND-IT'S-IN-THE-CABINET-UNDER-THE-STEREO . . .

SEE-IF-THERE-ARE-ANY-NOTES-FROM-HIS-TEACHERS-IN-HIS-LUNCH-BOX-ANY QUESTIONS?

THIS IS STACEY. SHE'S MY FRIEND. SHE'S BABY-SITTING FOR YOU TODAY.

I'LL BE BABY-SITTING SOMEWHERE ELSE, NOT FAR AWAY. I'LL BE BACK AROUND 5:00.

OH, STACEY, MY BIG BROTHERS ARE CHARLIE AND SAM.

CHARLIE IS 16 AND SAM IS 14.

THEY MIGHT BE AROUND THIS AFTERNOON, THEY MIGHT NOT. HAVE FUN, YOU GUYS!

SLAM!

. . . HI.

HI.

THEY'RE A BIT UNRULY.

OHHH. I KNOW ALL ABOUT UNRULY.

LET ME INTRODUCE MYSELF...

I'M MISS HARGREAVES, MRS. MCKEEVER'S NIECE. SHE'S OUT OF TOWN, AND I HAVE AN APPOINTMENT THIS AFTERNOON.

WE FIND WE NEED SOMEONE WITH PINKY AND BUFFY AT ALL TIMES.

WHAT DOES SHE EXPECT?

LET'S GO LET THEM OUT OF THE LAUNDRY ROOM. THEY'RE PROBABLY READY TO PLAY.

ALL RIGHT.

GET READY. THESE TWO MONSTERS OF MY AUNT'S WILL PRACTICALLY BREAK THE DOOR DOWN.

...ACK!

DO I HAVE TO WATCH THEM **PLUS** PINKY AND BUFFY?!

OH, MY DEAR! THOSE **ARE** PINKY AND BUFFY!

BUT... BUT I'M A **BABY**-SITTER, NOT A DOG-SITTER!

I DON'T KNOW WHAT ARRANGEMENTS MY AUNT MADE.

BUT HERE ARE THE DOGS, AND HERE **YOU** ARE, AND **I** HAVE TO LEAVE.

BUT... BUT...

GRAB!

WAAH!

Friday, September 26th

Kristy says we have to keep a record
of every baby-sitting job we do in this
book. My first job through the
Baby-sitters Club was yesterday. I was
sitting for Jamie Newton, only it
wasn't just for Jamie it was for
Jamie and his three cusins.
And boy were they wild!

* Claudia *

## Chapter 8

HI-HI!

HI, JAMIE!

OH! WHO ARE ALL OF YOUR FRIENDS?

HELLO, CLAUDIA . . . COME ON IN . . .

THAT'S MINE!

YANK!

NO, IT'S NOT! IT'S MINE!

HIIIII-YAH! I'M A NINJA! YOU'RE A DEAD MAN! I MEAN . . . DEAD LADY!!

SIGH.

AND THAT'S HOW CLAUDIA MANAGED TO TAME THE FELDMANS.

Saturday, September 27

   I don't know what Kristy always makes
such a fuss about. Watson's kids are cute.
I think Kristy would like them if she ever
baby-sat for them. Are you reading this,
Kristy? I hope so. Well, this notebook is for
us to write our experiences and our problems
in, especially our problems.

   And there were a few problems at
Watson's house...

                    Mary Anne

FIRST . . . HE BITES IF PROVOKED. AND SCRATCHES.

HE'S AN ATTACK CAT!

IT'S BEST IF YOU JUST STEER CLEAR OF HIM. I'D OFFER TO CONFINE HIM WHILE I'M GONE, BUT HE DOESN'T LIKE THAT MUCH.

HE GNAWED THE LAUNDRY ROOM DOOR ALL UP.

JUST TRY TO IGNORE HIM. AND **DON'T** TOUCH HIM!

I GUESS THAT'S IT. . . . ANY QUESTIONS?

WHAT ABOUT MRS. PORTER, DADDY?

OH, I THINK SHE'S ON VACATION, HONEY . . . NO NEED TO WORRY ABOUT HER.

MRS. PORTER IS AN ELDERLY WOMAN WHO LIVES NEXT DOOR. SHE'S A BIT ON THE ECCENTRIC SIDE. . . . KAREN IS CONVINCED SHE'S A WITCH.

SHE **ISN'T**, OF COURSE, BUT SHE DOESN'T LIKE ANIMALS, AND BOO-BOO SEEMS TO HAVE GOTTEN ON HER BAD SIDE.

WE TRY TO KEEP THE TWO OF THEM APART.

OKAY! I'M OFF. 'BYE, KAREN.

'BYE, DADDY.

'BYE, ANDREW.

'BYE.

SLAM!

WE'RE DIVORCED.

OUR PARENTS LIVE IN DIFFERENT HOUSES.

YUP.

YOU SEE THAT HOUSE?

THE ONE NEXT DOOR?

...YES?

THAT'S WHERE MRS. PORTER LIVES, AND SHE'S AN HONEST-AND-TRULY WITCH. HER WITCH NAME IS MORBIDDA DESTINY.

SHE'S ALREADY GONE FROM THE WINDOW!

SHE'S COMING TO THE DOOR, I KNOW IT!!

SIGH.

OKAY, OKAY.

KAREN, YOU'RE IN CHARGE OF ANDREW FOR A FEW MINUTES. I'LL BE RIGHT BACK.

MREOG

RAPSCALLION!

CHILDREN AND PETS... DARNED NUISANCE...

BOO-BOO!

DID YOU HEAR THAT? IT WAS A CURSE!

"RAPSCALLION"? NO, THAT ISN'T A CURSE. THAT'S A REAL WORD.

ARE YOU SURE?

LOOK... DID YOU SEE MORB -- MRS. PORTER MIXING UP HERBS OR LOOKING FOR BATS' FEET?

NO...

DID YOU SEE HER CRUSHING TOADSTOOLS OR STIRRING THINGS IN A CAULDRON?

...NO...

...BUT BOO-BOO'S GOING CRAZY!

HISSSSSS

OH, HE'S JUST BEING A CAT. CATS DO SILLY --

LOOK!

MORBIDDA DESTINY'S AT HER WINDOW AGAIN....

## Chapter 10

AT OUR NEXT MEETING . . .

OH, HI, MRS. MCKEEVER.

BUFFY AND PINKY WERE VERY NICE. BUT WE ARE **NOT** PET SITTERS. I'M SORRY.

HELLO, BABY-SITTERS CLUB.

GOOD AFTERNOON, BABY-SITTERS CLUB.

HEY, STACEY...

WHY DON'T WE FIGURE OUT HOW MUCH MONEY THE CLUB HAS EARNED SO FAR?

OKAY!!

$$
\begin{array}{l}
4 \\
+5.50 \\
\hline
9.50
\end{array}
\qquad
\begin{array}{l}
10 \\
+6 \\
\hline
16
\end{array}
$$

$5+5+5\ldots$

$2 \times 10 = 20$

$16.25 \div 3$
$\ldots$

138

WHAT'D HE BRING US THIS TIME? GREEK FOOD? ITALIAN?

NOTHING. HE'S HERE FOR LEFTOVERS.

HONEY, WOULD YOU PLEASE RUN UPSTAIRS AND PUT ON A DRESS?

A **DRESS!!** WHY?!

BECAUSE I'M THE MOMMY, THAT'S WHY.

PUT ON THE BLUE AND WHITE ONE WE JUST BOUGHT, OKAY?

OKAY.

THAT'S GREAT, MOM!

CONGRATULATIONS!

YEAH!

WHAT DOES THAT MEAN?

IT MEANS YOUR MOTHER WON'T EVEN LET ME GIVE HER AN ENGAGEMENT RING YET.

SMART MOVE, MOM.

BUT THAT I'M THINKING ABOUT IT.

BUT IF YOU GOT MARRIED . . . WHERE WOULD WE LIVE? WOULD DAD STILL GIVE YOU CHILD-SUPPORT MONEY?

I DON'T KNOW, HONEY. WE HAVEN'T THOUGHT THAT FAR AHEAD.

## Chapter 11

THERE GOES STACEY AND HER FAMILY, OFF TO NEW YORK.

SHE SAID THEY MIGHT BE BACK TOMORROW MORNING, BUT PROBABLY NOT UNTIL THE EVENING.

I THINK WE SHOULD WAIT TO HAVE THE PARTY. IT'LL BE MORE FUN IF EVERYONE'S THERE. WHAT ABOUT NEXT WEEKEND?

BUT WE REALLY WANT TO HAVE IT TOMORROW, RIGHT?

144

RING!

HELLO?

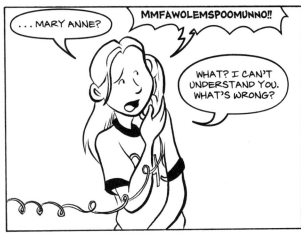

...MARY ANNE?

MMFAWOLEMSPOOMUNNO!!

WHAT? I CAN'T UNDERSTAND YOU. WHAT'S WRONG?

YOUR FATHER... WON'T LET YOU... SPEND YOUR MONEY... ON WHAT? ON THE **FEET** OF A **PAUPER?!**

...OH, ON THE **PIZZA** PARTY. OH, MARY ANNE. WHY NOT??

HE SAYS I SHOULD SAVE THE MONEY FOR MORE IMPORTANT THINGS. LIKE CLOTHES AND COLLEGE.

YOU MEAN YOU HAVE TO START PAYING FOR YOUR CLOTHES **YOURSELF?!**

I DON'T KNOW... HE JUST WON'T LET ME SPEND FIVE DOLLARS ON PIZZA. THAT'S ALL.

OKAY, WELL, WE'LL STILL HAVE $15 WHEN WE GET STACEY'S SHARE.

I GUESS THE FOUR OF US CAN MAKE DO WITH ONE LARGE PIZZA. STACEY PROBABLY WON'T EAT ANY, ANYWAY.

BUT, KRISTY, I'M NOT COMING TO THE PARTY NOW.

WHAT?! WHY NOT?!

I'M NOT LETTING YOU GUYS PAY FOR EV... JUST A SECOND...

OKAY, THANKS FOR HELPING ME WITH THIS MATH!

DID YOUR DAD JUST WALK IN? DO YOU HAVE TO GO?

YES! 'BYE, JUNE!

"JUNE"?

RING!

HELLO?

GUESS WHAT.

UH-HUH . . . OH . . . CLAUDIA, DON'T YOU GET ONE OF THOSE LETTERS FROM SCHOOL EVERY FALL?

YES, BUT THIS TIME DAD READ IT RIGHT BEFORE I TOLD HIM AND MOM ABOUT THE PIZZA PARTY.

SO NOW HE WANTS YOU TO SPEND **ALL WEEKEND** ON TEN MATH PROBLEMS?!

WELL, THAT AND ALL THE OTHER HOMEWORK I DIDN'T DO THIS YEAR.

I GUESS THE PARTY'S OFF.

MAYBE NOT . . . LET'S SEE IF STACEY COMES HOME IN TIME.

OKAY.

A FEW HOURS LATER . . .

RING....
RING....

HELLO?

MRS. MCGILL? HI! THIS IS KRISTY THOMAS . . . STACEY'S FRIEND. IS SHE THERE?

MUMBLE WHISPER

I'M SORRY, DEAR, STACEY'S NOT HOME.

OH. WHERE DID SHE GO?

WELL, SHE'S . . . UM . . . SHE STAYED IN NEW YORK WITH FRIENDS, KRISTY. SHE'LL BE BACK TOMORROW NIGHT.

THANKS.

RING!!

beep!

HELLO??

HI, IT'S ME.

-- HI!!! DID YOUR FATHER CHANGE HIS MIND??

ARE YOU KIDDING? I JUST WANTED TO BE SURE YOU KNEW STACEY WAS HOME. I WAS RIDING MY BIKE TO THE PIKES', THAT'S WHERE I AM NOW, THEY CALLED AND ASKED ME TO SIT THIS MORNING, AND THE MCGILLS PASSED ME IN THEIR CAR. STACEY DIDN'T SEE ME.

ARE YOU SURE YOU SAW STACEY IN THE CAR?!

POSITIVE.

RING!

HELLO?

KRISTY! ENOUGH WITH THE PHONE!

IT'S FOR YOU.

OH... HELLO.

WHAT? OH, NO. WELL, DAVID MICHAEL IS SICK.... THE BABY-SITTERS CLUB? I'LL CHECK WITH KRISTY. SURE. TWENTY MINUTES. SOMEONE WILL BE READY.

KRISTY, THERE'S A LITTLE EMERGENCY. WATSON NEEDS ONE OF YOU GIRLS IMMEDIATELY, TO SIT FOR HIS KIDS THIS AFTERNOON.

I'D TELL HIM TO DROP THEM OFF HERE INSTEAD, BUT I'M AFRAID THEY'D CATCH DAVID MICHAEL'S VIRUS.

OH, MOM! IT'LL HAVE TO BE **ME**!

## Chapter 12

THE EMERGENCY WAS THAT WATSON'S EX-WIFE HAD BROKEN HER ANKLE AND WAS IN THE EMERGENCY ROOM.

WATSON HAD TO GO OVER THERE AND DO SOMETHING ABOUT INSURANCE FORMS (I THINK), AND TAKE HER HOME AFTER, SINCE HER FUTURE SECOND HUSBAND WAS AWAY FOR THE WEEKEND.

THIS IS ANDREW AND KAREN. . . . THEY'RE ABOUT READY FOR THEIR LUNCH. . . . PEANUT BUTTER AND JELLY IS FINE. KAREN CAN HELP YOU FIND THINGS.

AROUND 2:00 ANDREW GOES DOWN FOR A NAP. . . .

I WISH I COULD SHOW YOU AROUND, BUT KAREN WILL HAVE TO FILL IN FOR ME.

OKAY, PUMPKIN?

OKAY!

HI, BOOPA-DE-BOO! THIS IS DADDY'S CAT. HE'S REAL OLD. DID YOU KNOW HE'S HAD TWO SPELLS PUT ON HIM BY THE WITCH NEXT DOOR?

MMM. COME ON . . . LET'S GET OUR LUNCH.

. . . YUM!! YUMMY-YUMMERS! YOU'RE A NEAT BABY-SITTER. YOU FIX GOOD FOOD.

YUP.

IS OUR MOMMY ALL RIGHT?

154

YOU'RE KRISTY, RIGHT?

RIGHT.

IS YOUR MOMMY ELIZABETH THOMAS?

THAT'S RIGHT.

MY DADDY SAYS HE LOVES YOUR MOMMY.

...I GUESS.

IF THEY GET MARRIED, YOUR MOMMY WILL BE MY MOMMY.

STEPMOMMY. I MEAN, STEPMOTHER. AND GUESS WHAT ... I'D BE YOUR STEPSISTER. AND YOURS, ANDREW.

YUP.

...I GUESS THAT WOULD BE OKAY.

160

162

## Chapter 13

MONDAY.

GUESS WHAT!

WHAT?

DAD AND I HARDLY TALKED TO EACH OTHER ON SATURDAY, BUT ON SUNDAY I TOLD HIM I'D BE EARNING A LOT OF MONEY THROUGH THE BABY-SITTERS CLUB, AND ASKED IF I COULD SPEND HALF OF IT ANY WAY I WANTED IF I PROMISED TO PUT THE OTHER HALF IN THE BANK! AND HE SAID YES!

SO IF WE HAVE THE PARTY, I CAN GO!!

THAT'S GREAT!

YOU REALLY STOOD UP TO YOUR DAD!

AND **I** CAUGHT UP ON ALMOST ALL OF MY HOMEWORK, AND I GOT A B-MINUS ON THOSE 10 MATH PROBLEMS! THEN I TALKED TO **MY** PARENTS. I TOLD THEM I WASN'T JANINE, AND THEY SAID THEY KNEW THAT . . . BUT THAT I SHOULD SET ASIDE AN HOUR AFTER DINNER EACH NIGHT FOR HOMEWORK . . . BUT THEY AND MIMI WILL HELP ME.

THAT'S GOOD! I'M PROUD OF US, AREN'T YOU?

YEAH! LICORICE STICK?

SO! STACE! HOW WAS NEW YORK?

OH, FINE. I WENT SHOPPING AND GOT THESE PANTS.

NICE.

HOW WERE YOUR FRIENDS?

FINE.

YOU KNOW, THE STRANGEST THING HAPPENED ON SATURDAY.

MARY ANNE SAW YOU COME HOME WITH YOUR PARENTS THAT MORNING. HOW COME YOU MADE YOUR MOM SAY YOU STAYED IN NEW YORK?

ARE YOU ACCUSING MY MOM OF LYING?!

...I GUESS SO.

HELLO, BABY-SITTERS CLUB.

YES? YES? OKAY. OKAY. SURE. I'LL CALL YOU BACK.

WHO'S FREE THURSDAY AFTERNOON? IT'S A SEVEN-YEAR-OLD KID, CHARLOTTE JOHANSSEN, ON KIMBALL STREET.

I'M FREE.

SO'M I.

ME, TOO.

ME, TOO.

WELL, NOW WHAT?

YEAH, WHOSE DUMB IDEA **WAS** THIS CLUB, ANYWAY?

SINCE THE CLUB WAS **MY** "DUMB" IDEA, I'LL TAKE THE JOB!!

HELLO, DR. JOHANSSEN?

COME ON, MARY ANNE. LET'S GO. I CAN SEE WE'RE NOT WANTED HERE.

KRISTY...

SAVE IT. I'M NOT SPEAKING TO YOU AT THE MOMENT.

THAT EVENING

ROAR!! GRARR!!

BAM BAM

MONOPOLY

SLAM!

SURPRISE!!

MONOPOLY

## Chapter 14

CLAUDIA?

HMPH.

DO YOU STILL WANT TO HAVE OUR CLUB MEETING TOMORROW?

...I GUESS SO. SURE.

OKAY... WE'LL SEE YOU THEN.

'BYE.

THAT NIGHT, FOR A CHANGE, MOM AND MY BROTHERS AND I WENT OVER TO WATSON'S FOR DINNER.

SO I'LL HAVE THREE BIG STEPBROTHERS, ONE BIG STEPSISTER...

A NEW STEPMOMMY... A NEW STEPDOGGY...

DINNERTIME!

173

SPEAR

DIP

SPLASH
#!

OOOOO! KRISTYYY!

HA HA HA!

KISS DADDY! KISS DADDY!

WEDNESDAY AFTERNOON

I'M SORRY I WAS MEAN BEFORE. I'M SORRY I YELLED.

THAT'S OKAY.

AND I'M SORRY I LIED.

CLAUDIA, ARE YOU ONLY SORRY ABOUT MAKING MARY ANNE CRY, OR ARE YOU ALSO SORRY YOU YELLED AT **ME?**

KRISTY, I'M SORRY I LOST MY TEMPER. I REALLY AM. BUT YOU MADE ME ANGRY.

HOW?

YOU **KNOW** HOW.

MY MOUTH GETS ME IN TROUBLE ALL THE TIME . . . JUST ASK MY MOTHER.

JUST ASK ANYBODY!

RING!

GOOD AFTERNOON . . . BABY-SITTERS CLUB!

SOON . . .

YOU GUYS? NOW THAT WE'VE ALL STRAIGHTENED OUT OUR PROBLEMS . . . I THINK WE SHOULD TRY TO HAVE THE PIZZA PARTY AGAIN.

STACE -- YOU **REALLY** DON'T HAVE TO WORRY ABOUT YOUR DIET. THE PIZZA PLACE MAKES REALLY GOOD SALADS.

AND . . . WE CAN HAVE THE PARTY AT **MY** HOUSE. . . .

OKAY!! I'LL BE THERE!

ALL **RIGHT!!**

HONEY, OF **COURSE** YOU CAN HAVE THE PARTY HERE!

IS IT OKAY IF WE HAVE A SLEEPOVER?

SURE. I LIKE THE BABY-SITTERS CLUB.

AFTER ALL . . . IT BROUGHT YOU AND WATSON CLOSER TOGETHER.

IS SATURDAY OKAY?

AND SO . . .

AND YOU PROBABLY HAVE TO GIVE YOURSELF INSULIN SHOTS EVERY DAY. IT'S ROTTEN, BUT I MEAN, YOU'RE NOT A FREAK OR ANYTHING. WE'LL QUIT OFFERING YOU CANDY, OKAY?

BUT... DON'T YOU GUYS CARE?

OF COURSE WE CARE.

I MEAN, DOESN'T IT BOTHER YOU?

NO. WHY SHOULD IT?

I DON'T KNOW. MY MOTHER ACTS LIKE IT'S SOME KIND OF CURSE. THE KIDS AT MY OLD SCHOOL STARTED TEASING ME ABOUT MY DIET, AND BECAUSE I FAINTED A COUPLE OF TIMES.

SO MOM DECIDED WE SHOULD COME TO A "PEACEFUL LITTLE TOWN"... YOU KNOW, GET ME TO SOMEPLACE CIVILIZED AND QUIET.

THAT'S WHY YOU MOVED HERE??

YUP. WELL, PARTLY.

WOW.

SO I THOUGHT MAYBE I SHOULD COVER UP WHAT WAS WRONG WITH ME. MOVING HERE SEEMED LIKE A CHANCE TO START OVER.

BUT **NOT** TELLING YOU GUYS WAS WORSE THAN TELLING MY OLD FRIENDS.

WELL . . . YOU DON'T HAVE TO TELL **ALL** THE KIDS. WE KNOW, BUT WE SEE YOU MOST OFTEN.

MAYBE YOU COULD SORT OF KEEP QUIET ABOUT IT AT SCHOOL . . . BUT NOT LIE ABOUT IT.

THAT'S TRUE.

THANKS, YOU GUYS.

I THINK WE SHOULD HAVE A SLUMBER PARTY ONCE A MONTH.

YEAH, AND WHEN MOM AND WATSON GET MARRIED, WE'LL HAVE THEM AT WATSON'S HOUSE.

WHEN YOUR MOTHER AND WATSON GET **MARRIED?!**

OH, THAT'S RIGHT! I HAVEN'T TOLD YOU GUYS YET!

KNOCK KNOCK

HEY, ALL YOU GIRLS! MOM SAID TO BRING THIS TO YOU.... DON'T WORRY, I'M NOT COMING IN....

YOUR BROTHER IS **SO** CUTE, KRISTY!!

I GUESS.

WE WERE FRIENDS AGAIN.

OUR CLUB WAS A SUCCESS, AND I, KRISTY THOMAS, HAD MADE IT WORK... OR, HELPED TO MAKE IT WORK.

I HOPED THAT MARY ANNE, CLAUDIA, STACEY, AND I -- THE BABY-SITTERS CLUB -- WOULD STAY TOGETHER FOR A LONG TIME.

# Ann M. Martin's

The Baby-sitters Club is one of the most popular series in the history of publishing, with more than 175 million books in print. She is also the author of the acclaimed novels *Belle Teal*, *A Corner of the Universe* (a Newbery Honor Book), *Here Today*, and *A Dog's Life*. She lives in New York.

# Raina Telgemeier

grew up reading comics, baby-sitting, and reading The Baby-sitters Club in San Francisco. She graduated from the School of Visual Arts in New York City. Her comics have been nominated for the Ignatz and Eisner Awards, and her illustrations have been featured in magazines, books, and newspapers. Raina currently lives in Queens, New York.